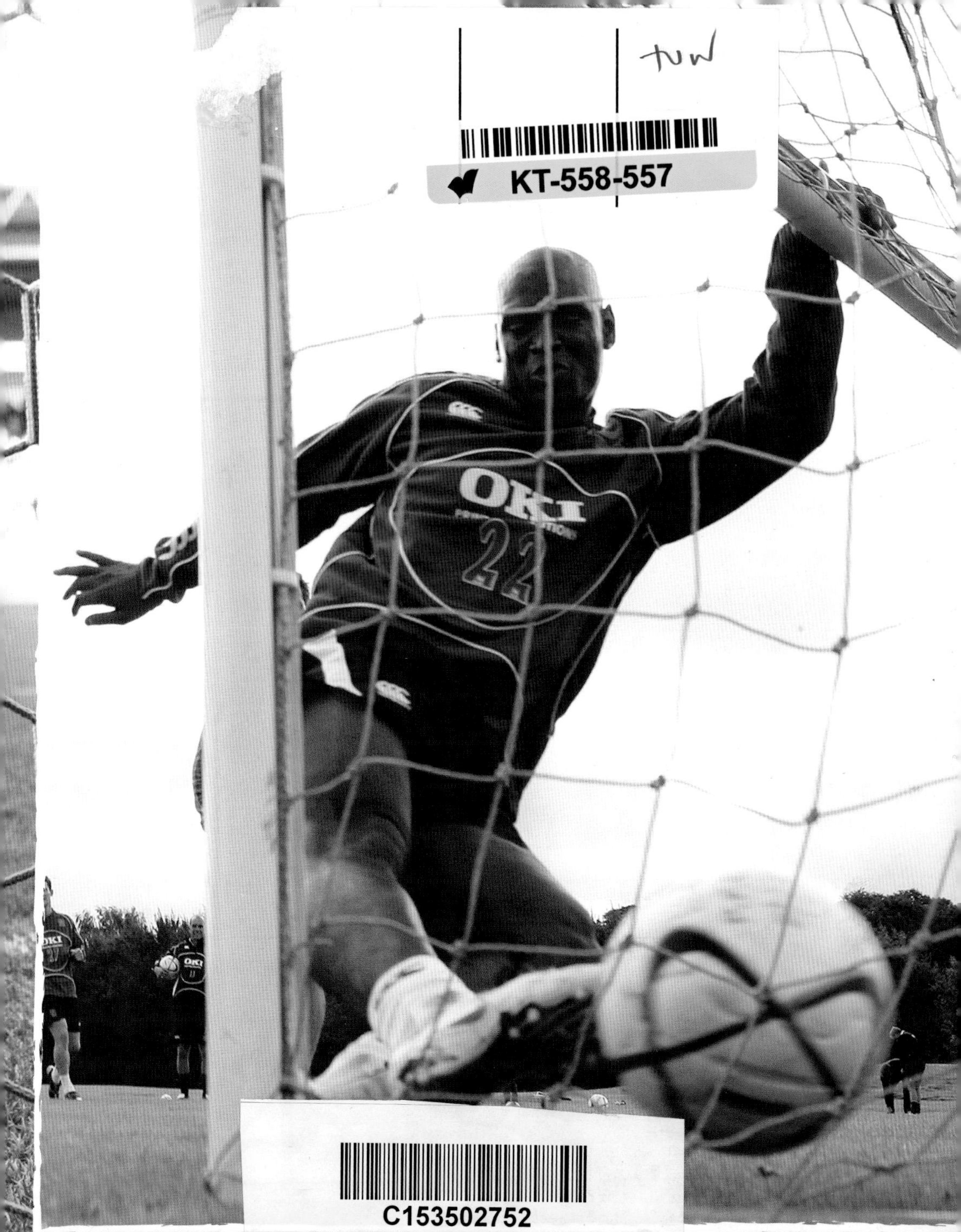

Get the ball into the net.

Nod it!

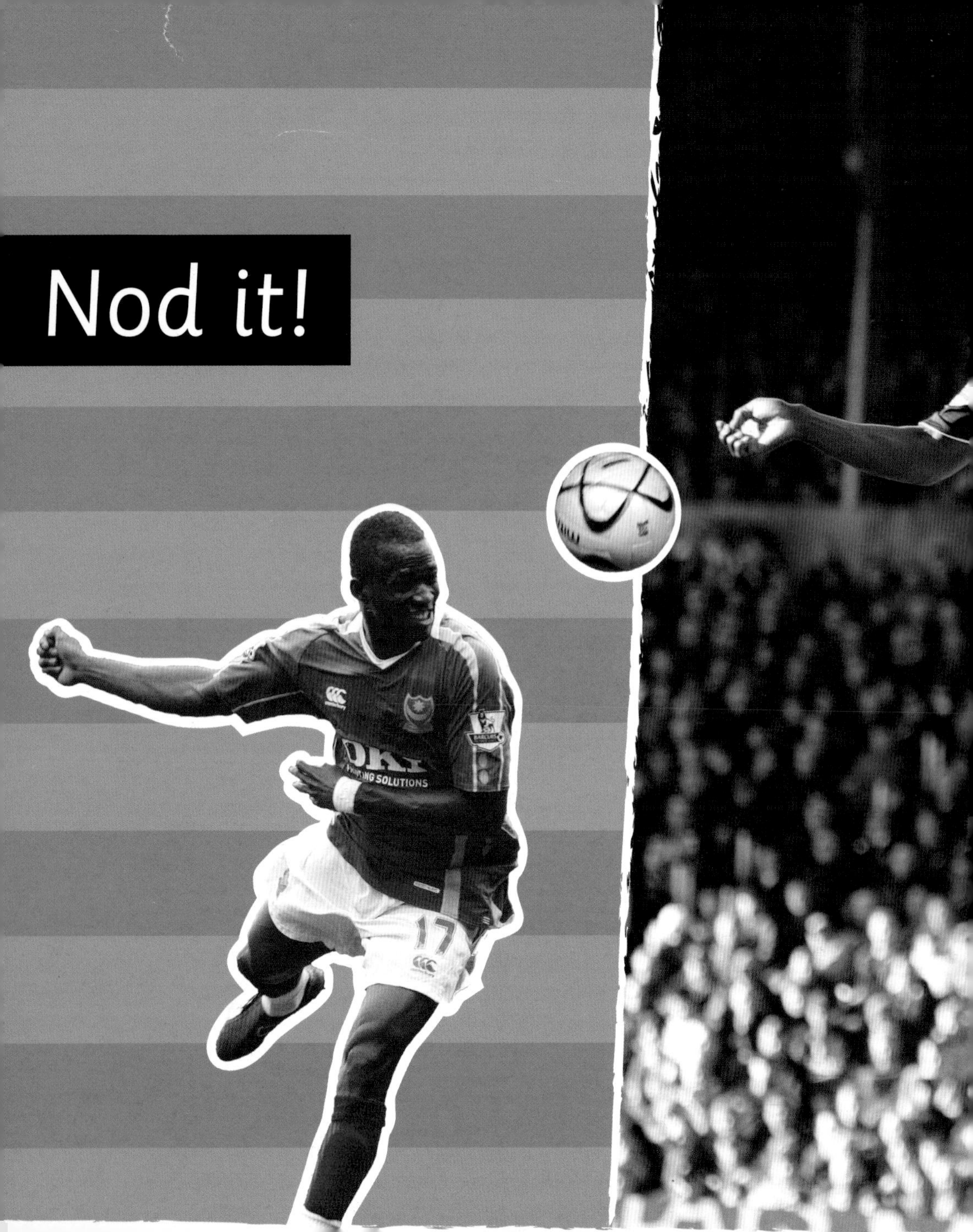

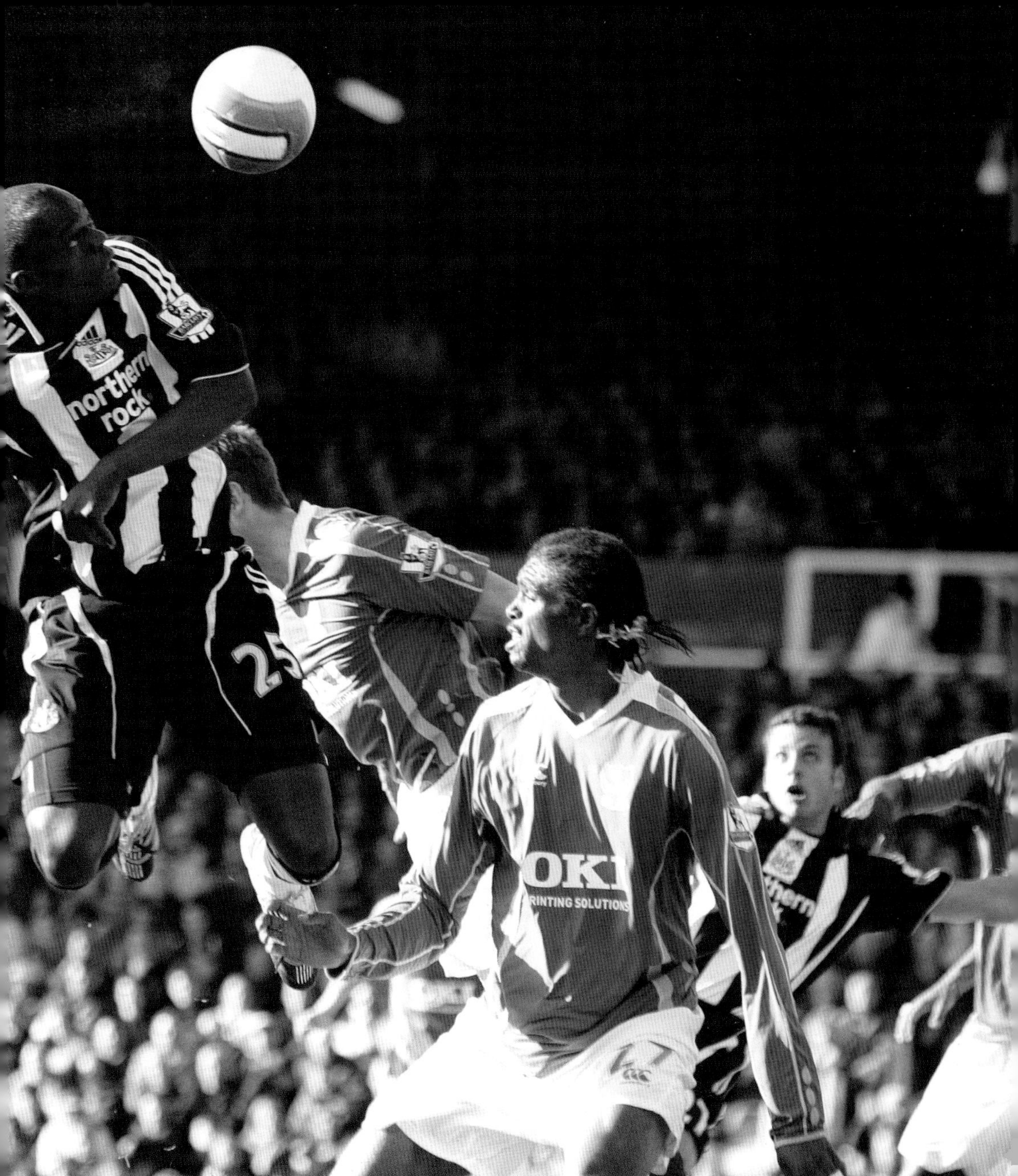
northern rock
OKI
PRINTING SOLUTIONS

Tap it.

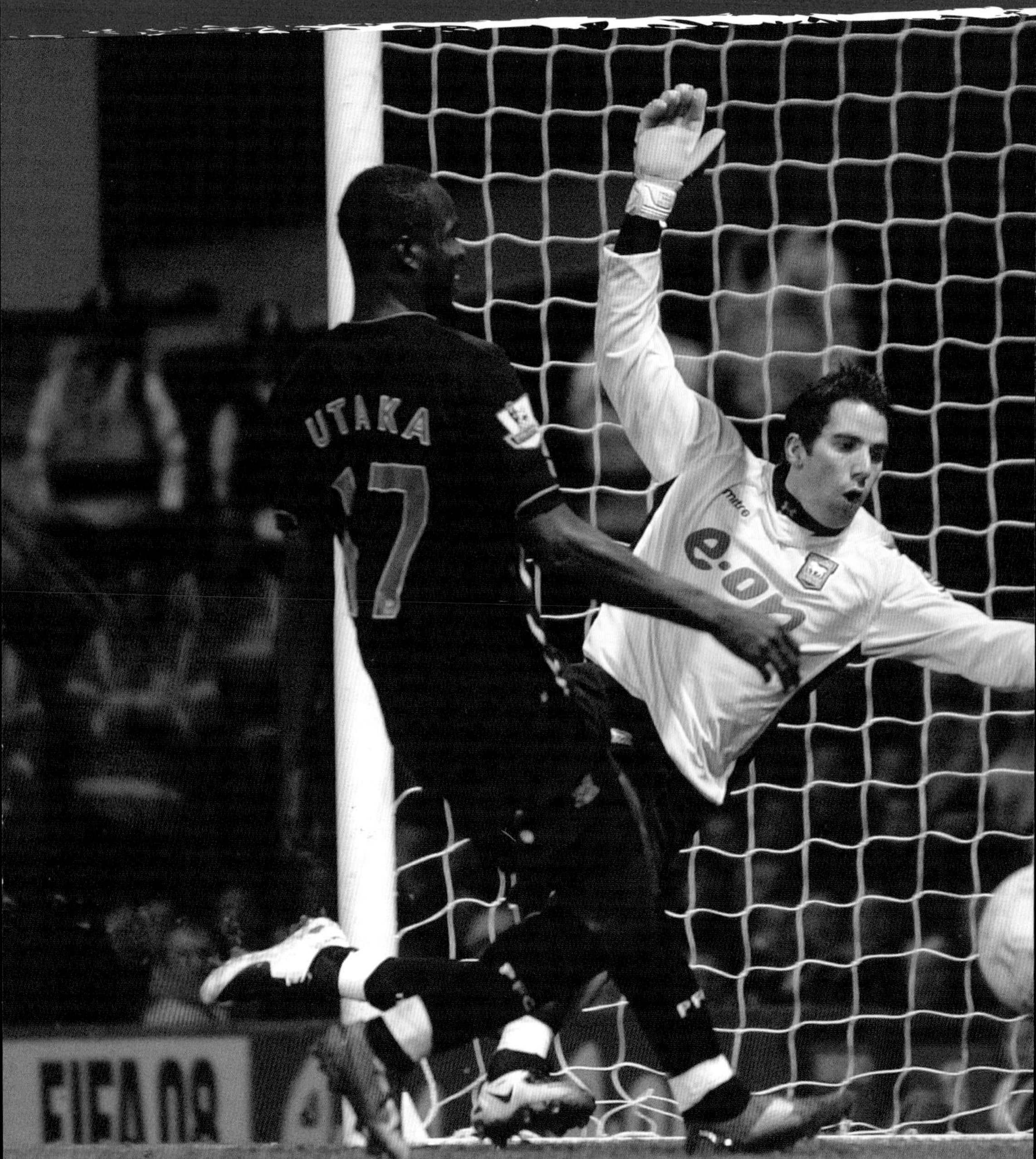

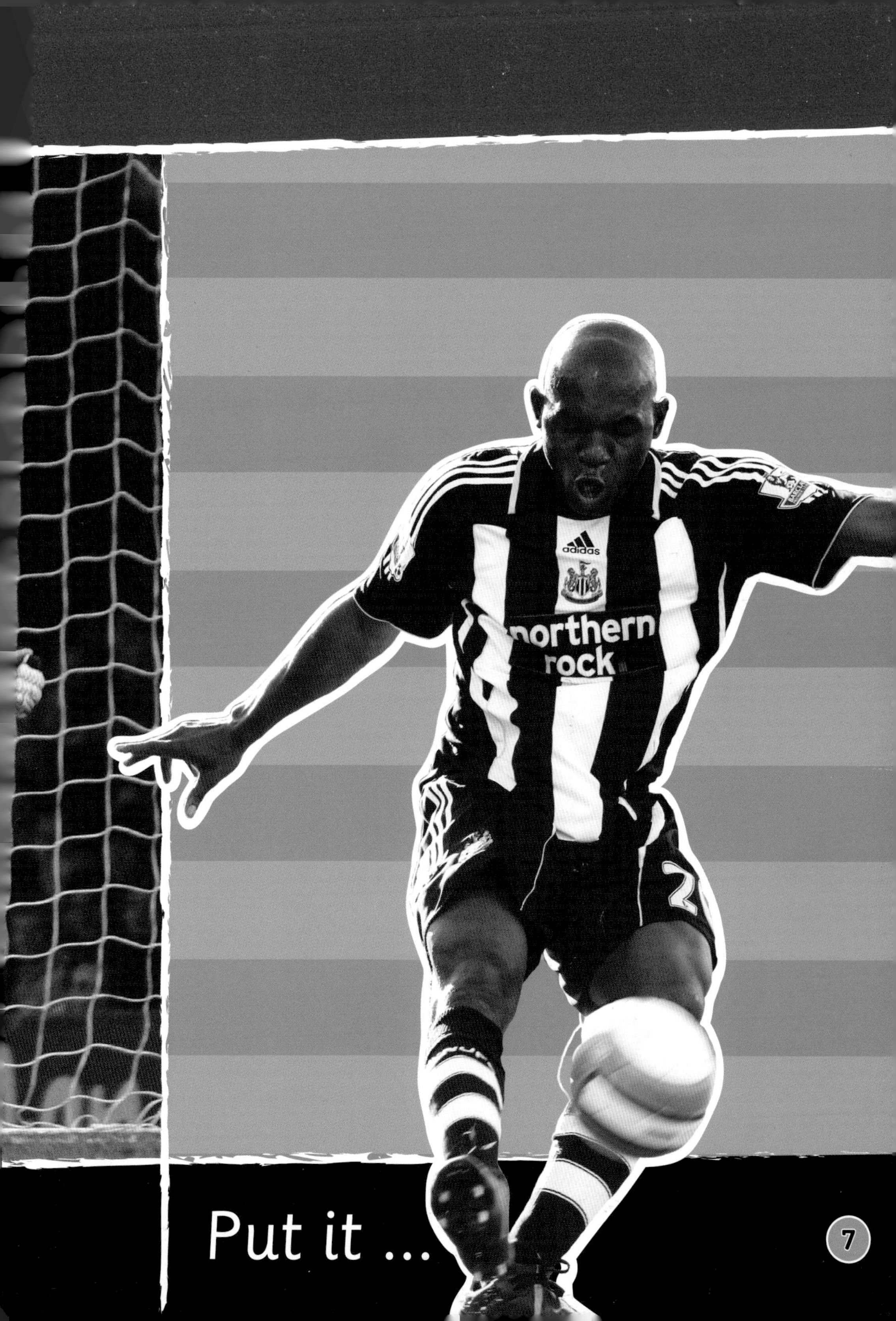
adidas
northern rock

Put it ...

Kick it ...

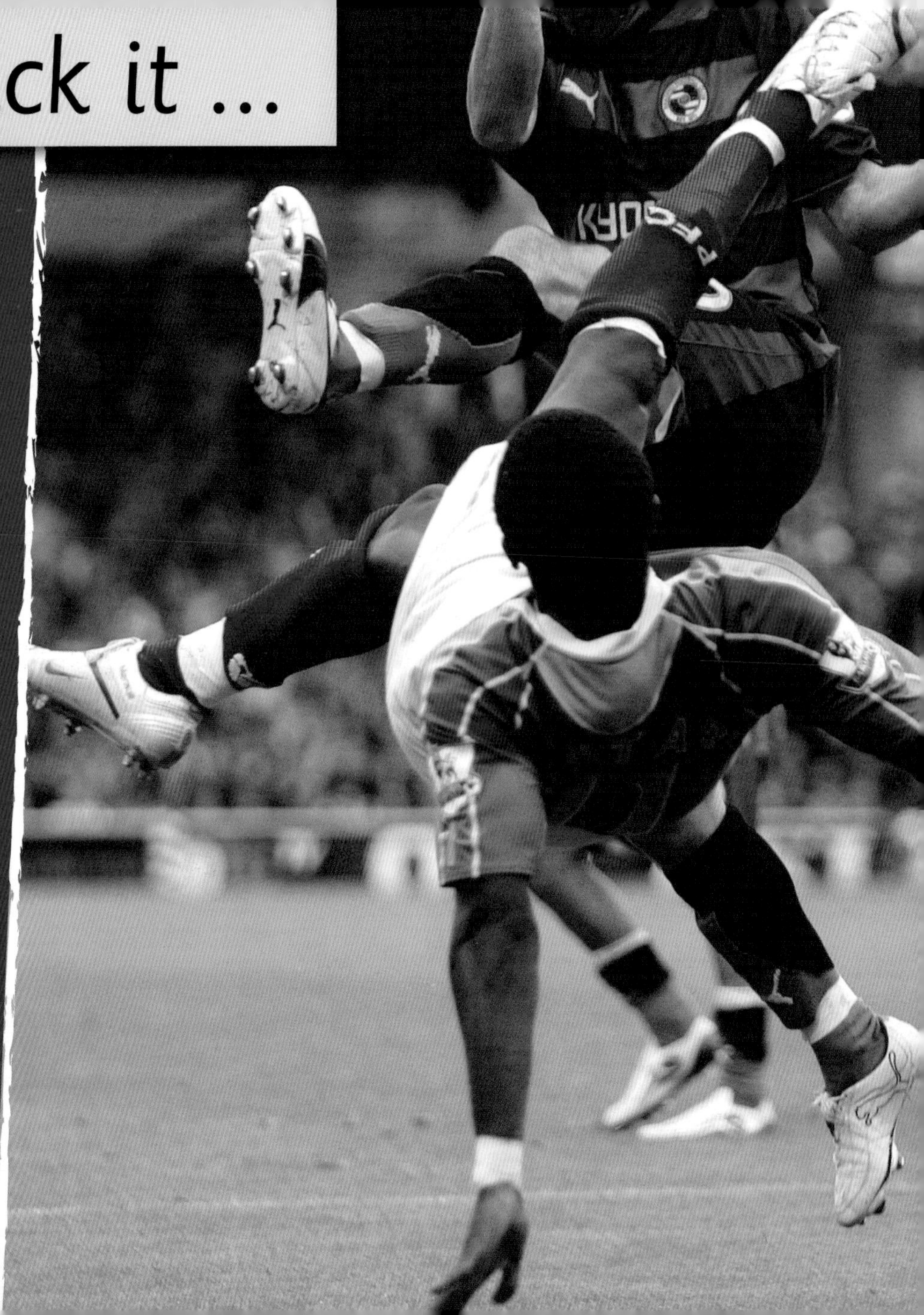

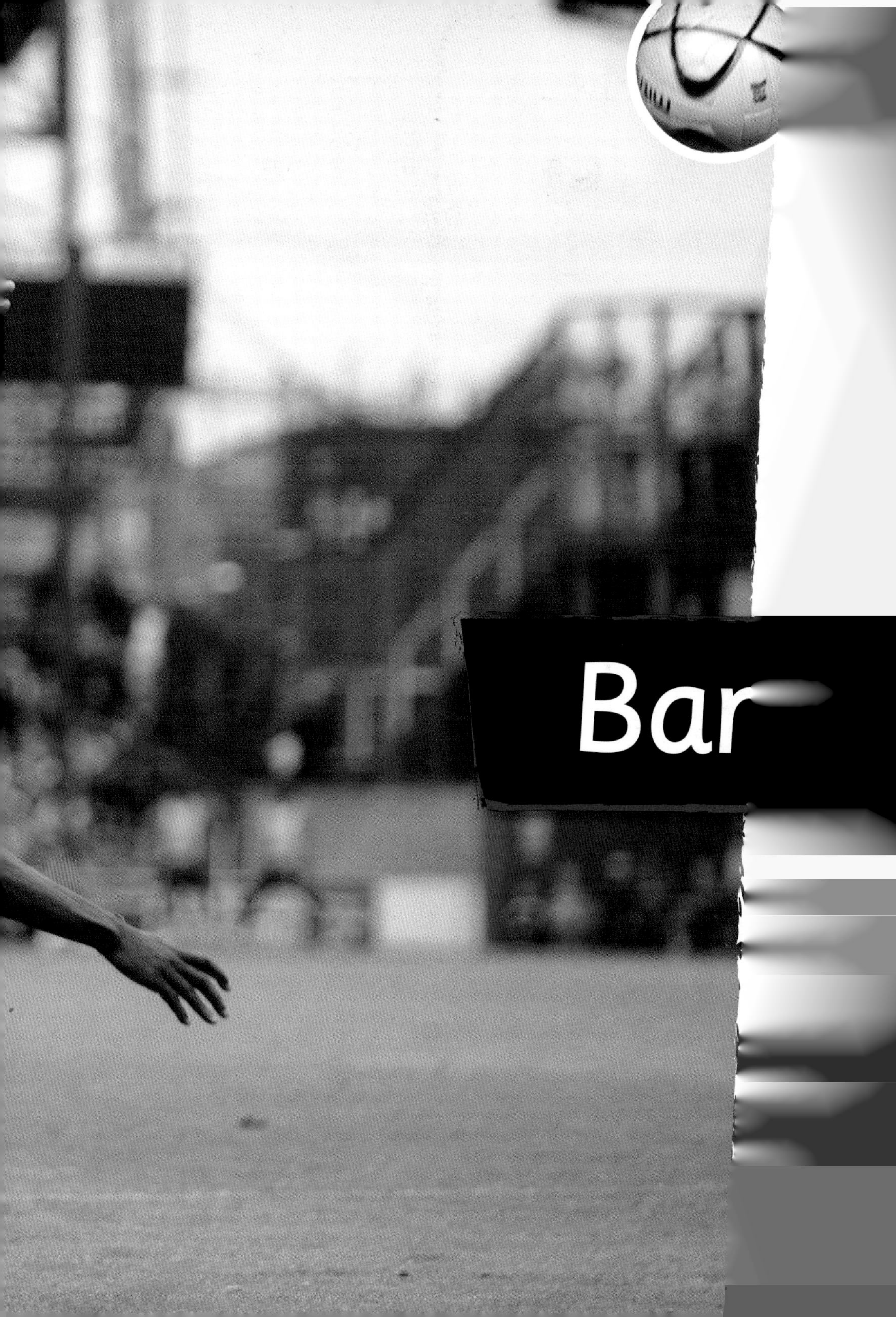
Bar

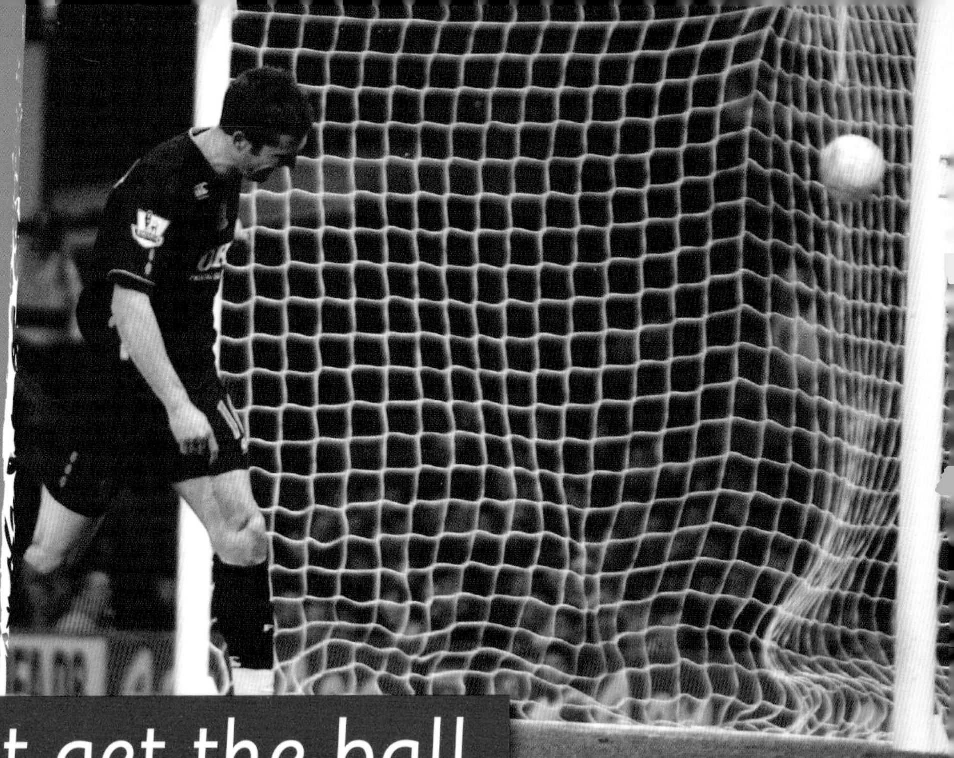

Just get the ball into the net!

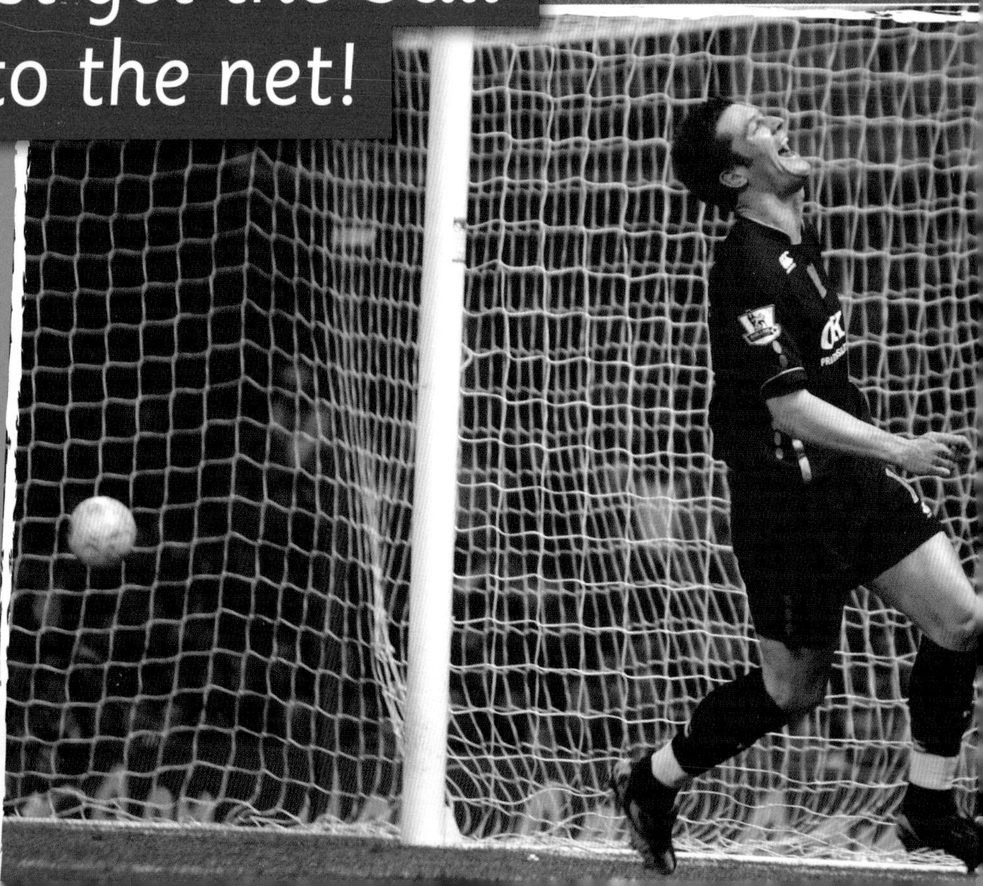